Contents

Danny's diary

Saturday

I'm here with Great Aunt Daisy. She's my mum's aunt, and she lives by the sea.

The beach here looks great, and there's a pier. I think I'm going to like it.

Sunday

We went to the beach today, and Aunt Daisy gave me the money to get an ice-cream from the pier. It was very breezy.

There was an artist selling pictures, and he was painting a picture of the sea.

It was when I went to look at it that it happened. The wind blew my ice-cream on to the picture that he was painting! The artist turned and shouted, but I just ran!

3

Monday

It was wet when I woke up this morning, but Aunt Daisy said never mind, I could help her tidy the cupboard under the stairs.

The under-the-stairs cupboard was full of surprises. I had fun with some old hats. It was wet all day and we couldn't go to the beach.

Tuesday (morning)

It was still wet this morning. I found a box of photographs in the cupboard under the stairs. They were old, and some of the pictures were in an album.

Aunt Daisy told me there were some photographs of Mum as a little girl in there. It's stopped raining now, so we're taking the album to the beach this afternoon to look at.

Tuesday (afternoon)

We sat on the pier this afternoon. The sun was out, but it was very breezy again. I was carrying the photograph album.

Aunt Daisy told me to be careful with it, because she didn't want her pictures to get lost.

I was careful. But I fell over and dropped the album. Some of the pages blew away and I ran after them. Luckily, Aunt Daisy didn't see me. But one page blew across the pier . . . and I saw the artist pick it up.

I didn't go after it.

I didn't want to meet him.

Wednesday

The album is back in the cupboard under the stairs now.

Perhaps I should say something to Aunt Daisy about the missing page, but she might be cross.

We went to the beach today. When I wanted an ice-cream, I didn't go to the pier, I went the other way.

7

Thursday

Aunt Daisy has found out about the missing picture!

This is how it happened. Aunt Daisy wanted to go on the pier this afternoon. I tried to hide from the artist, but Aunt Daisy went to look at his pictures. And she got a surprise.

There was a picture of a beautiful young woman with long red hair – and it was her! It was Aunt Daisy as a young woman! She could hardly believe it!

Aunt Daisy told the artist. He smiled. Then he said he thought he had something that was hers. And he gave her the page from the album.

Aunt Daisy asked him where he had got it, and the artist told her that the wind blew it his way. He had painted the picture from one of the photographs. Aunt Daisy looked at me.

The pier artist looked at me — and he knew I was the "ice-cream" boy. But then he laughed.

I had to tell Aunt Daisy about the missing picture, but luckily she wasn't cross.

Friday

Mum came to take me home today.

She asked if I'd had a good time, and I told her it was great staying with Aunt Daisy. She wanted to know what I'd done, and I told her it was a long story.

But it's here in my diary.

She can read it, if she likes.

Morse code

A ·–   B –···   C –·–·   D –··

E ·   F ··–·   G ––··   H ····

I ··   J ·–––   K –·–   L ·–··

M ––   N –··   O –––   P ·––·

Q –––·   R ·–·   S ···   T –

U ··–   V ···–   W ·––   X –··–

Y –·––   Z ––··   ? ··––··   *full stop* ·–·–·–

People all over the world use the Morse code. In this
code, dots and dashes stand for the different letters of
the alphabet. You can use Morse code to send a
message to someone you can't speak to or write to.

You can use your foot or a stick to tap out a message in Morse code. A heavy tap stands for a dash, and a light tap stands for a dot.

You can use Morse code to send a message in the dark to someone who can't hear you. You need a torch or a light to flash on and off. A long flash of light stands for a dash, a short flash stands for a dot.

Prisoners can tap Morse code messages on the water pipe.

When someone wants to send a secret message they can use Morse code. Spies can use it to signal to each other.

A prisoner can tap out a message on the wall or the water pipe. Then someone in another part of the prison can hear the message.

This man is sending a Morse code message over the radio.

The man who first thought of the Morse code lived in America. People could send their message along a line like a telephone line. Now we can use radio to send these messages. People use Morse code on ships all over the world to talk to each other.

The most well known message in the world is the signal for help. It has just three letters, S O S. In Morse code it looks like this: ... ——— ...

Message for a burglar

Nikki heard the news on the radio. There had been a burglar at a house in their road.

"Will the burglar come here?" she asked her mum.

"No," said Mum. "We've got good strong locks on our windows."

The door bell rang. It was Lee, the boy from upstairs. He wanted Nikki to come and play.

"You can go," said Mum. "I have to go shopping." She took her basket and went out.

"Let's go and play in the garden," said Lee.

As they went outside, Nikki saw a bit of paper on the steps.

"What does it say?" Lee asked.

"It's just letters and numbers. I can't read it," Nikki said. She showed Lee the paper.

2LBS POT
POL
WNW CL
TEA

"It looks like a secret message in code," Lee said.

"Perhaps it's been left by the burglar," said Nikki. "We must work out what it means."

"2LB must be my flat," said Lee. "My flat is number 2 and LB stands for my name, Lee Brown. The burglar is coming to my flat!"

"SPOT comes next. That means to look. POL is short for *police*. So SPOT POL means look out for the police," said Nikki.

She read the last bit of the message.

"WNW and CL must be *window* and *closed*. He's going to break in through a closed window. And he's coming at tea-time," said Nikki.

"We'll catch him," said Lee. "Let's hide in the garden."

The two friends hid in the hedge behind a pile of leaves and sticks. They sat there all afternoon. It began to rain, and they both got cold and wet.

At last they heard someone coming. They saw feet go up the steps and stop at the door.

Nikki and Lee couldn't keep still any longer. They jumped out from behind the hedge.

"Got you!" they shouted.

But it wasn't a burglar, it was Nikki's mum. She looked very surprised to see them.

"What on earth are you two up to?" she asked. Lee showed her the message.

"It's in code," said Nikki. "It says the burglar is going to break into Lee's flat."

Nikki's mum looked at the message. Then she started to laugh.

"This isn't a secret message!" she said. "I wrote this! It's my shopping list. I dropped it on my way out. Look – 2LBSPOT – that stands for 2 pounds of potatoes. POL stands for polish, and WNW CL stands for window cleaner. TEA, well, that's just tea."

She showed them the potatoes, the polish, the window cleaner and the tea in her basket.

Nikki and Lee felt very silly that they had been wrong about the message.

"Never mind. You were very clever to try to work out the code," said Nikki's mum.

They all went in to have a hot drink. When Nikki and Lee were warm again they laughed about the mix-up.

"I'm really glad that it wasn't a burglar after all," said Lee.

"But don't write any more shopping lists in code, Mum," laughed Nikki.

Michelle

I lived in a street where there weren't any other children. One day, a new girl came to live in our street. I was very pleased. I would have someone to play with at last.

I went out on my bike. The new girl was in the garden. She was stroking her cat.

"Hello," I said. "My name's Ella. What's yours?"

The new girl didn't answer.

"Do you want to play with me?" I asked.

The new girl didn't even turn round. She just went on stroking her cat.

"I've got a cat too," I said. "Perhaps your cat and mine will be friends."

The new girl saw me then. She didn't speak at all but stared and stared and stared. I went home and told my mum.

"That new girl is no fun at all," I said. "I asked her to play with me and she wouldn't even speak to me."

"Perhaps she's very shy," said Mum.

The next day, I saw Mum talking to the new girl's mum.

Later, Mum told me that the new girl's name was Michelle, and that she was deaf.

"What if she is deaf?" I said. "She can still talk, can't she?"

"That's difficult," said Mum. "How can you learn to talk if you can't hear your own voice?"

"Can't she hear her own voice?" I said.

"Hardly at all," said Mum. "Not even with hearing aids. She can't hear anyone's voice very much."

I thought about the new girl. I closed my eyes, trying to feel what it was like to be blind. Then I tried to close my ears. I couldn't. Even if I put my hands right over my ears I could still hear my own voice when I shouted.

"So won't I have anyone to play with after all?" I said.

"You might," said Mum. "Michelle does have a way of hearing. She hears with her eyes."

"How can you hear with your eyes?" I asked.

"Watch," said Mum. Then Mum began to speak. I saw her mouth moving but she made no sound at all.

"What did I say?" asked Mum.

"I don't know," I said. "You didn't use your voice."

"Michelle would have understood me," said Mum. "She can lip read."

We played a lip reading game. Some words were easy to guess. Others were difficult.

"Also," said Mum, "Michelle has a way of talking. She talks with her hands. Her mum is going to show us how."

Later that week, Michelle and her mum came to tea. Michelle looked at the cake and rubbed her tummy to show that she was hungry.

"I'm hungry, too," I said.

Then she showed me the sign for *cake*, *eat* and *good*. They were easy to understand.

After tea, Michelle's mum showed us how to spell words on our fingers.

Mum and I practised the finger spelling alphabet. At first it was difficult, but then it became easier.

The next time I saw Michelle, she was putting on her roller boots. I touched her arm.

"Hello," I said, so that she could read my lips.

Michelle smiled. Then I spelt my name on my fingers. Michelle spelt hers. Then we both played with our roller boots.

"Our cats are friends," she signed. "We can be friends too."

Michelle soon started at our school. I was playing with my friends and Michelle came over.

"Can I play?" she signed.

My friends didn't want to play with Michelle. They made fun of her because she couldn't hear or talk very well. But I played with Michelle. We did some finger spelling together. My friends came to watch.

"What are you saying?" they asked.

"I won't tell you," I said. "It's our secret language."

But on the way home, I did tell my friend Sam. I showed him how to spell his name. Then Kay wanted to know how to spell her name. Then Jake. Soon they could all finger spell their names.

Later, a special teacher came for Michelle. She taught us all how to finger spell and she taught us some signs. It was great fun. We made up some signs of our own. We could all talk as much as we liked without making any noise.

Michelle is good fun too. The more signs we learn, the more we can talk to each other. The more we can talk to each other, the more she smiles. And she's great on roller boots!

The finger spelling alphabet

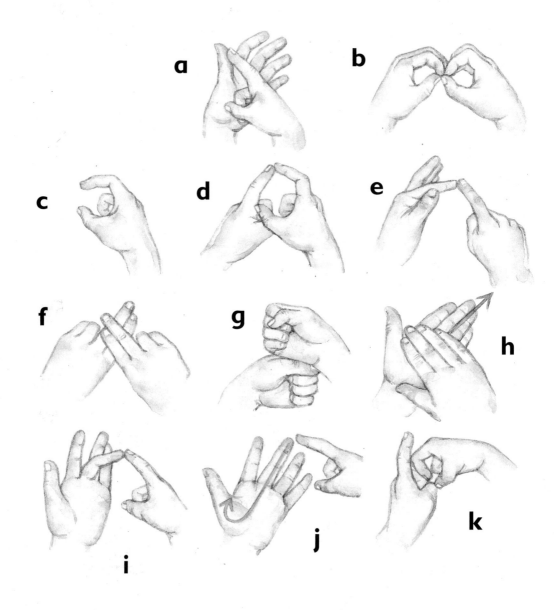

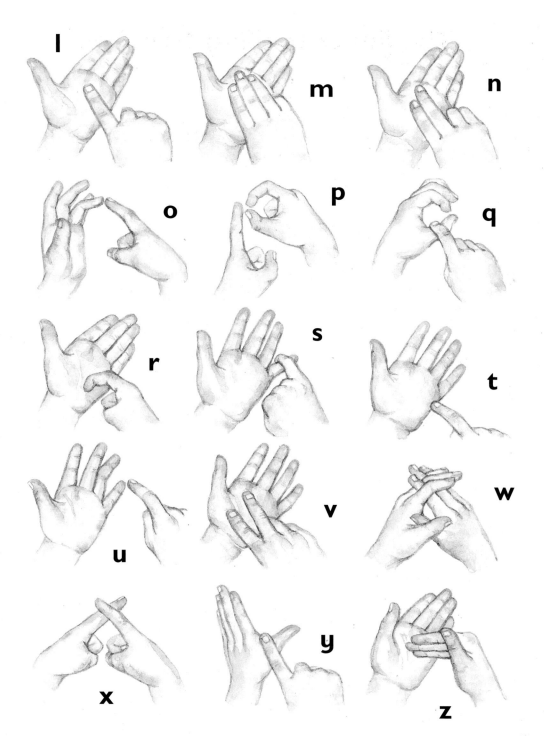

l

m

n

o

p

q

r

s

t

u

v

w

x

y

z

Mystery girl

Dear Anna,

Somebody is living in your old flat now. She is about 25. I said hello the other morning, and she said hello back. She was carrying a big bag and went off down the street. I was with Carly Brown, playing with a frisbee. Carly said the girl looked funny!

Write and tell me about your new flat.

Love,

Jenny

Dear Jenny,

    Our flat is in a big house and we have the back garden to play in. I'm going to go to work in the flower shop with Mum every day while it's the summer holiday. The shop is in the city precinct.

    Can you find out more about the girl in our old flat?

Love,

Anna

Dear Anna,

 I still don't know any more about the girl in your old flat. She goes out every morning at 11 o'clock, carrying her bag, and comes back at 3 o'clock. I'm going to call her Mystery Girl.

 Carly says she's a bank thief!

Love,

Jenny

Dear Jenny,

I like coming to the shop, and sometimes I help Mum to make up a basket of flowers. There are street entertainers in the middle of the precinct. Some come every day, but others come just some days. There are four young men who play music in the afternoon, and this morning there was a fire-eater! There's a clown who juggles as well.

Perhaps Carly is right. Perhaps Mystery Girl is a bank thief. She may be carrying the money in that bag when she comes home in the afternoon!

Love,

Anna

Dear Anna,

A burglar has been going into flats and houses round here over the last week, and the police say it's always late morning or early afternoon. Well, you can guess what Carly said, can't you? That Mystery Girl is a burglar because she's always out at that time. I told Carly she was silly, but she could be right.

I've never seen a fire-eater.

Love,

Jenny

Dear Jenny,

One of the street entertainers came in to buy some flowers for his girl-friend.

The clown has a painted mouth, a red wig and baggy trousers. He juggles, can hop on one hand, and can play sad but beautiful music on the mouth organ. Mum says it makes her want to cry!

But all this is not as exciting as living near a burglar, if that's what Mystery Girl is.

Love,

Anna

Dear Anna,

　　Carly and I followed the Mystery Girl this morning, and she just went to the bus stop and caught a bus into the city. So she can't be the burglar, can she? Carly says she could still be a bank thief.

　　Funny you should write about a mouth organ, because we can sometimes hear somebody playing one in your old flat.

Love,

Jenny

Dear Jenny,

Guess what! Early this afternoon, the clown came in to buy some flowers for her mum's birthday. That's right, <u>her</u> mum! The clown is a girl! With her painted mouth and red wig, you couldn't tell. She comes late in the morning every day, then goes home early in the afternoon.

Wait! You don't think...?

Dear Anna,

Mystery Girl talked to me this morning. I said hello, and wasn't it a lovely day. And she said yes, it was her mum's birthday, and she was going to get her some flowers. And she smiled!

I didn't ask her about the mouth organ music, but I've been thinking about it. You see, that's sad and beautiful and – wait! You don't think...?